Feel the Heat

Description

Students explore the phenomenon of temperature difference between sun and shade on a surface on the school grounds. They carry out an investigation of temperatures of surfaces around their school in the sun and in the shade to see if shady surfaces are cooler than surfaces that are in the sun. Then, they design, build, and test physical models of shade structures that could provide a place to stay cool on the playground.

Alignment With the *Next Generation Science Standards*

Performance Expectations

K-PS3-1: Make observations to determine the effect of sunlight on Earth's surface.

K-PS3-2: Use tools and materials to design and build a structure that will reduce the warming effect of sunlight on an area.

K-2-ETS1-2: Develop a simple sketch, drawing, or physical model to illustrate how the shape of an object helps it function as needed to solve a given problem.

Science and Engineering Practices	Disciplinary Core Ideas	Crosscutting Concepts
Planning and Carrying Out Investigations With guidance, plan and conduct an investigation in collaboration with peers. Using Mathematics and Computational Thinking Describe, measure, and/or compare quantitative attributes of different objects and display the data using simple graphs. Constructing Explanations and Designing Solutions Use tools and/or materials to design and/or build a device that solves a specific problem or a solution to a specific problem. Generate and/or compare multiple solutions to a problem.	PS3.B: Conservation of Energy and Energy Transfer Sunlight warms Earth's surface. ETS1.B: Developing Possible Solutions Designs can be conveyed through sketches, drawings, or physical models. These representations are useful in communicating ideas for a problem's solutions to other people.	Cause and Effect Events have causes that generate observable patterns. Scale, Proportion, and Quantity Relative scales allow objects and events to be compared and described (e.g., bigger and smaller, hotter and colder, faster and slower).

Continued

Alignment With the Next Generation Science Standards (*continued*)

Science and Engineering Practices	Disciplinary Core Ideas	Crosscutting Concepts
Analyzing and Interpreting Data Use observations (firsthand or from the media) to describe patterns and/or relationships in the natural and designed world(s) in order to answer scientific questions and solve problems. Analyze data from tests of an object or tool to determine if it works as intended.		

Note: The activities in this lesson will help students move toward the performance expectations listed, which is the goal after multiple activities. However, the activities will not by themselves be sufficient to reach the performance expectations.

Featured Picture Books

TITLE: **Summer Sun Risin'**
AUTHOR: **W. Nikola-Lisa**
ILLUSTRATOR: **Don Tate**
PUBLISHER: **Lee & Low Books**
YEAR: **2005**
GENRE: **Story**
SUMMARY: *Rhythmic poetry and beautiful paintings depict a little boy enjoying a summer day on his family's farm in Texas in the 1950s. The illustrations trace the Sun as it travels across the sky from sunrise to sunset, while the text describes the family's daily ritual of chores and how the hot Sun affects their lives.*

TITLE: **Sun and Shade**
AUTHOR: **Mary Lindeen**
PUBLISHER: **Norwood House Press**
YEAR: **2017**
GENRE: **Non-Narrative Information**
SUMMARY: *This Beginning-to-Read book explains that the Sun is a star that gives off heat and light. Life on Earth is dependent on the Sun's heat and light, but there can be negative effects of too much sunlight. Blocked sunlight makes a shadow called shade that can protect living things from getting too much sunlight.*

Time Needed

This lesson will take several class periods and will need to be taught on sunny days during the warmer months of the school year. Suggested scheduling is as follows:

Session 1: Engage with Summer Sun Risin' Read-Aloud and Explore with Comparing Temperatures

Session 2: Explain with Comparing Temperatures and Sun and Shade Anticipation Guide and Read-Aloud

Session 3: Elaborate with Keep It Cool Design Challenge: Building Our Models

Session 4: Evaluate with Keep It Cool Design Challenge: Testing Our Models

Materials

For Comparing Temperatures (for teacher use only)

- Infrared laser thermometer (noncontact, not designed for measuring body temperature) (Note: Infrared laser thermometers, sometimes called "temperature guns," can be purchased at Amazon.com, Walmart, or hardware and home improvement stores for $20–$60.)

For Keep It Cool Design Challenge

- Cooler of ice (Note: Take the cooler of ice outside with you and hand out the ice cubes when it is time to begin testing designs.)
- 2 ice cubes of the same size and shape (per pair)
- 2 condiment cups or small plastic cups to hold one ice cube each (per pair)
- A towel to sit on if activity is done on blacktop
- Flashlight (per pair)
- A variety of shade-structure building supplies such as the following (per pair):
  - Construction paper
  - Index cards, cardboard, or both
  - Pieces of cloth or felt
  - Clear materials such as clear plastic lids and plastic wrap
  - 4 or more straws
  - 4 or more craft sticks
  - Roll of masking tape
  - Scissors

SAFETY

An infrared laser thermometer is a device that can measure the temperature of an object or surface. The laser beam included in this type of device does not measure the temperature; it helps the user aim the device at the desired object. Because a laser beam is involved, you should be very cautious when using it.

- Follow all usage and safety guidelines included in the packaging.
- Do not allow students to use the device. Do not point it toward people.
- Do not point it at a highly reflective surface, such as a mirror.
- Some school districts and states prohibit the use of lasers in the classroom or field. Always check school district policy and state regulations relative to laser use before doing this activity.
- Use caution in working with scissors, sticks, and so on. They can be sharp and cut or

Student Pages

Background for Teachers

The Sun, our nearest star, is the source of virtually all energy on our planet. Without the Sun's energy, there would be no light, no heat, and no life on Earth. The Sun is an enormous burning ball of gases nearly a million miles across. In terms of scale, if Earth were the size of a pea, the Sun would be about the size of a beach ball! By studying the color of the light emitted from the Sun, scientists have concluded that the surface of the Sun is about 10000°F. The Sun is very far from Earth—about 93 million miles away—but it appears so big and bright to us because it is much closer than neighboring stars.

We can feel the Sun's heat warm our skin and the blacktop, we can see the visible light that comes from the Sun, and we can see the effects of damaging ultraviolet light on our skin. But how do all these types of energy get to Earth when the Sun is so far away? The Sun transfers energy to Earth through empty space by radiation, a form of energy transfer that does not require a medium. Traveling at the speed of light, energy released by the Sun reaches Earth in a little more than 8 minutes. This energy, known as electromagnetic radiation, consists of many different wavelengths, including visible light, ultraviolet light, radio waves, and even x-rays. Fortunately, the atmosphere prevents most of the dangerous wavelengths of energy (gamma rays, x-rays, and most ultraviolet light) from the Sun from reaching Earth's surface. Different surfaces can either reflect or absorb sunlight to various degrees. As a surface (such as your skin or the blacktop on the parking lot) absorbs sunlight, the sunlight forces the molecules in the material to move faster, thus warming the surface. Different types of land (green grass, beach sand, bare soil, pavement) can have different temperatures within the same area.

The temperatures of land and water in the same area may differ, even when they are exposed to the same amount of energy from the Sun. Land warms up at a faster rate than water and gets hotter. It also cools down faster than water. It is this uneven heating of Earth's surface that contributes to an imbalance of air pressure, which in turn causes wind and weather.

The Sun can be a big problem for city dwellers. Cities are often significantly warmer than the surrounding landscapes because urban surfaces absorb more sunlight than natural landscapes. Human activity in cities such as the use of air conditioning, vehicle emissions, and industry also plays a part. The difference between outside air temperatures in a city and its surrounding rural areas can be 9°–16°F or more in summer months. This phenomenon is called the "urban heat island effect."

Urban planners and architects are finding ways to counteract the heat island effect by selecting building materials such as "cool roofs" and pavements that are more reflective and by using trees and engineered shade structures. We all know how precious shade can be, especially during hot summer months. Creating shade over an area can greatly reduce the warming effects of the Sun. Installing engineered shade structures in public areas can help keep people feeling more comfortable when it is very hot outside (as well as protect people from the Sun's damaging ultraviolet rays). Although the air temperature in a sunny area might be about the same as the air temperature in a shaded area nearby, shade structures block or filter sunlight, which in turn makes surfaces cooler (no sunlight to absorb). In fact, the area beneath the canopy or roof of a shade structure can be 20°–25°F cooler than an area

that is exposed to the Sun. We feel cooler in the shade for the same reason the surface does—we're not being exposed to direct sunlight!

For primary students, laying a foundation for eventually learning about sunlight, weather and climate, climate change, and other concepts pertaining to the transfer of the Sun's energy to Earth systems involves making simple observations about the warming effects of the Sun. In this lesson, students explore the phenomenon of the temperature difference in the sun and shade. They do this by making qualitative observations of how warm it "feels" in the sun versus the shade and collect quantitative data by measuring the temperature of the same surfaces in the shade and then in the sun. Temperature data are collected using a handheld infrared laser thermometer, which measures surface temperatures more quickly and accurately than traditional classroom thermometers (see safety notes in the "Materials" section).

This lesson also incorporates engineering design. Students design and build a model of a playground shade structure. A model is a representation of an object, phenomenon, or system. A model can show how a design will look and how different parts work together. Models can be maps, diagrams, blueprints, flow charts, computer simulations, or three-dimensional physical models. Engineers use models to plan, test, and show others their ideas. Using their knowledge of the warming effects of sunlight, students build and test a physical model of a shade structure to keep cooler on the playground. A shade structure can help keep playground equipment cool, prevent kids from overheating, protect them against sunburn, and even help them play longer outdoors.

A simple extension of this lesson might be to walk around the school grounds and brainstorm ideas for keeping the area cooler during the hotter months (e.g., by replacing darker surfaces with lighter-colored materials and installing shade structures or planting trees in certain places). Exploring ways that scientists and engineers are working to design solutions for problems such as helping people stay cooler in outside areas brings science and engineering together in the classroom.

Learning Progressions

Below are the DCI grade band endpoints for grades K–2 and 3–5. These are provided to show how student understanding of the DCIs in this lesson will progress in future grade levels.

DCIs	Grades K–2	Grades 3–5
PS3.B: Conservation of Energy and Energy Transfer	• Sunlight warms Earth's surface.	• Energy is present whenever there are moving objects, sound, light, or heat. When objects collide, energy can be transferred from one object to another, thereby changing their motion. In such collisions, some energy is typically also transferred to the surrounding air; as a result, the air gets heated and sound is produced. • Light also transfers energy from place to place.
ETS1.B: Developing Possible Solutions	• Designs can be conveyed through sketches, drawings, or physical models. These representations are useful in communicating ideas for a problem's solutions to other people.	• At whatever stage, communicating with peers about proposed solutions is an important part of the design process, and shared ideas can lead to improved designs.

Source: Willard, T., ed. 2015. The NSTA quick-reference guide to the NGSS: Elementary school. Arlington, VA: NSTA Press.

National Science Teaching Association

engage

Summer Sun Risin' Read-Aloud

Connecting to the Common Core
READING: LITERATURE
KEY IDEAS AND DETAILS: K.1

ENGAGING WITH SUMMER SUN RISIN'

Inferring

Show students the cover of Summer Sun Risin' and introduce the author, W. Nikola-Lisa, and illustrator, Don Tate. Show them the front and back covers and ask

? Where do you think this story takes place? (Students will likely guess that the story takes place on a farm.)

? What clues from the cover make you think that? (There are chickens, crops, and a scarecrow.)

? What do you know about the Sun in the summer? How does it affect your daily activities? (Answers will vary.)

Read the book aloud, or share the pictures as you have the author sing the book aloud! His SoundCloud version is available online (see "Website" section at the end of this chapter).

Questioning

After reading, ask

? What did you notice about the pictures of the Sun in the book? (Answers will vary. Flip through the pages to show how the Sun starts on the left-hand page near the horizon, travels across the sky, and ends up on the right-hand side sinking down into the horizon.)

? Why do you think the Sun appears again in the very last picture? (It is the next day, so the Sun is rising again.)

? Why do you think the author used words such as shinin', glarin', blazin', and burnin' to describe the Sun? (The Sun is very hot. Heat comes from the Sun.)

? What do you think the author was trying to show about the Sun in his poem? (how the Sun makes things hot on a summer day; how it is a big part of our lives, especially in the summer; how it affects people all day long, etc.)

? How do you think the Sun affected the boy throughout the day? (It made him hot.)

Making Connections: Text to Self

Ask

? Have you ever felt the Sun blazin', burnin', and glarin'? (Answers will vary. Remind students to never look directly at the Sun!)

? How do you keep cool on a hot summer day? (sit in the shade, drink cold water, swim, eat ice pops)

? What is the effect of sunlight on our playground? In other words, are some areas of the playground hotter than others? (Answers will vary. Students may have noticed that some places on the playground get hotter than others, such as the surface of the slide, the blacktop area, and the seats of the swings.)

Tell students that next, they are going to have the opportunity to explore how the Sun heats different surfaces in different ways.

COMPARING TEMPERATURES

SEP: Planning and Carrying
Out Investigations
Plan and conduct an
investigation in collaboration
with peers.

explore

Comparing Temperatures

Ahead of time, identify four separate surfaces on the playground or elsewhere on school grounds that are partly shaded (e.g., grass, blacktop, cement, mulch).

Give each student a copy of the Comparing Temperatures student page and a clipboard, and have them write the names of the four surfaces you have selected in the first column of the table. (You may want to write these in before you make copies.) Tell them that they will be investigating the temperatures of these four surfaces. Ask

? What ways could we measure the temperatures of these four surfaces? (by feeling and then comparing them or by measuring their temperature with a thermometer)

Share that they will be comparing how warm these surfaces feel and measuring the surfaces' temperatures with a special type of thermometer. The temperatures will be recorded on their data tables in degrees Fahrenheit. Point out the °F symbol on the data table. Demonstrate how the infrared laser thermometer works by aiming it at the floor and measuring the temperature (follow all usage and safety guidelines included in the packaging). Tell them that because the thermometer uses a laser beam for precise aiming, students may not use it. Laser beams, even small ones such as those used in classroom pointers, cat toys, and the infrared laser thermometer, can be dangerous if pointed at the eye.

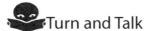Turn and Talk

Before you take the students outside, ask

? Which surface do you think will be the warmest? (Answers will vary.)

? Why do you think so? (Students will likely have had prior experience with shady versus sunny surfaces and may also have noticed relative temperature differences between darker and lighter surfaces.)

Have students discuss their thoughts with a partner, then ask a few pairs to share with the entire class.

Next, take students outside with their clipboards. Visit the shaded part of the first area together, and have students place their hands on the surface. Ask them to describe how the surface feels to the touch—cold, cool, warm, or hot. Measure the temperature of the surface with the infrared laser thermometer, and have students record the result in the "Temperature in Shade" column. Then, move to the sunny part of the same area and have students place their hands on the same surface in the sun. Ask them to compare how the same surface feels in the sun, and describe it as hotter or colder than the same surface in the shade. Then, measure the temperature with the infrared laser thermometer, and have students record the result in the "Temperature in Sun" column. Repeat the procedure for the rest of the surfaces.

National Science Teaching Association

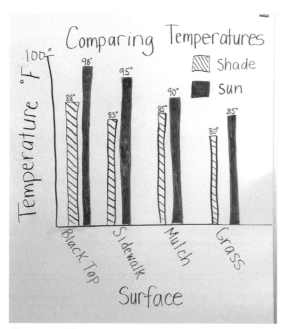

COMPARING TEMPERATURES BAR GRAPH

explain

Comparing Temperatures

Connecting to the Common Core
Mathematics
MEASUREMENT AND DATA: K.MD.2

Next, return to the classroom and give students the opportunity to share observations with a partner.

Turn and Talk

? What did you discover?

? What surprised you?

? What questions do you have?

After students have had the opportunity to share with a partner, discuss as a class.

Have students look at their data tables and compare the sun and shade temperatures of each surface. Have students circle the higher temperature for each one. Next, ask

? Do you notice a pattern for where each surface was hotter? (Students should realize that for each surface, the part in the sun was hotter than the part in the shade.)

? Why do you think the part in the sun was hotter than the part in the shade for all these surfaces? (Sunlight warms the surfaces. Sunlight was blocked from the shady parts.)

Optional Math Extension

Explain that sometimes it is helpful to graph data to find patterns. Create a bar graph titled "Comparing Temperatures" to display the data with "Surface" on the x-axis and "Temperature" on the y-axis. For each surface, there will be two bars of data, so have students help you create a key for sun and shade (e.g., yellow for sun and a darker color for shade). Have students help you determine how to draw the bars on the graph.

After completing the graph together, ask

? Which surface was the warmest? What is your evidence? (Students should know to choose their answer by observing which bar is the highest.)

? Why do you think so? (Answers will vary.)

? Which surface was the coolest? What is your evidence? (Students should know to choose their answer by observing which bar is the lowest.)

? Why do you think so? (Answers will vary.)

? What other observations can you make about our graph? (Answers will vary.)

Then, ask

? What is warming these surfaces outside our school? (the Sun)

Sun and Shade Anticipation Guide and Read-Aloud

Connecting to the Common Core
Reading: Informational Text
KEY IDEAS AND DETAILS: K.1

Determining Importance

Tell students that they are going to learn more about how the Sun warms the Earth by reading a nonfiction book titled Sun and Shade. Show students the cover and introduce the author, Mary Lindeen. Model how you can often find more information

about the author by looking in the back of the book. Read the short bio of the author, who is a former elementary school teacher.

Project a copy of the Sun and Shade anticipation guide. Pre-assess the students' understanding of the Sun by having them signal (thumbs-up or thumbs-down) to indicate whether they agree or disagree with each of the following statements. They should also write their guesses in the blanks on the student page. Tell them that at this point, they should just make their best guesses. After reading the book, they will be revisiting the anticipation guide to see if their guesses were correct.

1. The Sun is a star.
2. The Sun is made of rock.
3. The Sun gives off heat and light.
4. Plants need the Sun's light to grow.
5. Blocked sunlight makes a shadow called shade.

Have students signal when they hear evidence from the text for or against any of the five statements. Stop and discuss each one as you read the book aloud. The correct answers are as follows:

1. The Sun is a star. (true—p. 5)
2. The Sun is made of rock. (false—p. 6; the Sun is made of hot burning gases)
3. The Sun gives off heat and light. (true—p. 6)
4. Plants need the Sun's light to grow. (true—p. 8)
5. Blocked sunlight makes a shadow called shade. (true—p. 14)

Explain that although the Sun is so far away from us (93 million miles), we can feel the heat it produces. Energy from the Sun heats us, the air, the ground—everything on Earth. Refer to the Comparing Temperatures activity in the explore section and ask

? Were all the surfaces the same temperature outside our school? (no)

? What was different about the surfaces? (They were in different places, some were in the Sun

and some were in the shade, and they were different textures and colors.)

Explain that some surfaces absorb more sunlight than others, and that makes them warmer than the surrounding surfaces. For example, darker colors (such as blacktop) absorb, or take in, more sunlight than lighter colors (such as concrete). Ask

? Why do you think the shade was cooler than the other surfaces? (The sunlight was blocked.)

? What was blocking the sunlight in the shady area? (Answers will vary.)

Next, on the bottom of their anticipation guides, have students draw a picture of something they saw outside that made shade. They should include the Sun and the shaded area in their drawings. When students are finished, have them share and explain their drawings to others. Encourage them to ask questions and look for similarities and differences in their drawings.

elaborate

Keep It Cool Design Challenge: Building Our Models

SEP: Designing Solutions
Use tools and materials to design and build a device that solves a specific problem.

Ask

? Remember the boy in the story Summer Sun Risin'? How did the Sun affect him? (It made him hot.)

? How did he protect himself from the heat of the Sun? (He wore a hat.)

? What else could help him stay cool during a hot day? (shade, a cold drink, a fan)

? Do you ever get hot playing on our school's playground? (Answers will vary.)

? Where do you go to cool off? (Answers will vary.)

? Do you think you could design a structure for the playground that would reduce the warming effect of the Sun on you and your classmates? (Answers will vary.)

? What kind of structure would help you keep cool on the playground? (something that makes shade)

Present the following problem to students by writing it on the board and reading it aloud: "Problem: We need a place to cool off on the playground."

TESTING A SHADE STRUCTURE

Tell students that they are going to have the opportunity to solve this problem through engineering. They will be working with a partner to design a structure to provide a place to cool off when they are on the playground. Tell students that when engineers design something, they often build a model and test it before they build the real thing. Explain that a model is a representation of a real object. The model they build will not be big enough for real people to be underneath. It will be small, no bigger than a shoebox, but it will show the shape and features of a real structure. You may want to project a Google image search of "public shade structures" and have students notice the wide variety of shapes, sizes, and materials used to create public shade structures. Explain that they will be testing their structure by placing one

ice cube in a small cup inside the structure and another ice cube in an identical cup outside of it to see which ice cube melts first.

Show them one of the small cups that will be used to hold their ice cube and tell them that they need to make sure that the cup can fit underneath their structure. Then show the options you have gathered for materials. Ask

? What materials created the shady spots we observed outside? (playground equipment, trees, trash cans)

? What is similar about these materials? (They do not let all the light pass through.)

? What kinds of materials are best for creating shade? (materials that do not let light pass through)

? How could we test the materials provided to see how much light comes through? (We can hold them up to a flashlight, table lamp, or window to see if light passes through the materials.)

Let them experiment with the flashlight and materials. Then, ask

? Which of these materials can be used to create shade? (cardboard, index cards, construction paper, fabric, etc.)

? Why? (because the light does not pass through)

? Which of these materials is not as good at creating shade? (clear plastic lids, plastic wrap, etc.)

? Why? (because the light passes through)

Next, ask

? What will your structure look like?

? What materials will you use? Why?

? Where will you place the ice cube? Why?

Provide students with the various options for supplies (see "Materials" section) and let them begin building. You can give them the cups now so they can make their structure tall enough for the cup to fit underneath. Set a time limit, and visit groups as they work, reminding them that the structure must be tall enough for an ice cube to fit underneath.

evaluate

Keep It Cool Design Challenge: Testing Our Models

When all students have finished their structures, go outside on a sunny day to test them. Remember to take a cooler of ice with you! (You may want to have students bring a towel to sit on if you are doing this activity on blacktop.) Give each student the Keep It Cool Design Challenge student page and a clipboard. Ask

? How will we know if our models solved the problem of providing a place to cool off on the playground? (If it works, the ice cube inside the structure will stay frozen longer or be less melted than the one outside the structure.)

Have students set up their models in a sunny area. Encourage them to rotate their models and find the best angle to position them (the angle that provides the most shade). Then, give each pair two ice cubes of the same size and shape. Tell them to place one ice cube inside the model and one beside it. As students are waiting for the ice cubes to melt, have them each draw a picture of their model on the student page.

Connecting to the Common Core
Writing
TEXT TYPES AND PURPOSES: K.2

Writing

After waiting long enough to see a difference, have students compare the two ice cubes and answer the questions on the student page. For the first question, they need to circle which ice cube took longer to melt. For the second question, they need to write "yes" or "no" about whether their structure worked. For the third question, they need to write a sentence explaining how they know it did or didn't work. An example of an acceptable response would be "I

know it worked because the ice cube in the model did not melt as fast as the ice cube in the sun."

Have students compare their designs and discuss that there are multiple solutions to every problem. Then, have them brainstorm some ideas to improve their designs. If time allows, give students an opportunity to improve their designs and test the models again.

> **SEP: Designing Solutions**
> Compare multiple solutions to a problem.

STEM Everywhere

Give students the STEM Everywhere student page as a way to involve their families and extend their learning. They can do the activity with an adult helper and share their results with the class. If students do not have access to these materials at home, you may choose to have them complete the activity at school.

Opportunities for Differentiated Instruction

This box lists questions and challenges related to the lesson that students may select to research, investigate, or innovate. Students may also use the questions as examples to help them generate their own questions. These questions can help you move your students from the teacher-directed investigation to engaging in the science and engineering practices in a more student-directed format.

Extra Support

For students who are struggling to meet the lesson objectives, provide a question and guide them in the process of collecting research or helping them design procedures or solutions.

Extensions

For students with high interest or who have already met the lesson objectives, have them choose a question (or pose their own question), conduct their own research, and design their own procedures or solutions.

After selecting one of the questions in this box or formulating their own questions, students can individually or collaboratively make predictions, design investigations or surveys to test their predictions, collect evidence, devise explanations, design solutions, or examine related resources. They can communicate their findings through a science notebook, at a poster session or gallery walk, or by producing a media project.

Research

Have students brainstorm researchable questions:

? What is inside a glass thermometer? How does it work?

? What does the color of a star tell you about its temperature?

? What are some ways engineers are designing buildings and parking lots to keep cities cooler?

Continued

Opportunities for Differentiated Instruction (*continued*)

Investigate

Have students brainstorm testable questions to be solved through science or math:

? Does the shape or size of an ice cube affect how fast it melts?

? What heats up faster in the sun: a cup of water or a cup of sand?

? Does different-colored clothing have different surface temperatures in the sun?

Innovate

Have students brainstorm problems to be solved through engineering:

? Can you design a way to make s'mores with the Sun's energy?

? Can you design a cup to keep your drink cold on a hot day?

? Can you design a container to keep an ice pop frozen on a hot day?

Website

 W. Nikola-Lisa's SoundCloud version of *Summer Sun Risin'* https://soundcloud.com/nikolaplays/summer-sun-risin

More Books to Read

Bodach, V. K. 2012. *Gráficas de barras/Bar graphs*. Hacer gráficas/making graphs. Mankato, MN: Capstone Press.
Summary: This book describes in both Spanish and English how to create a bar graph and why bar graphs can be useful for comparing totals quickly.

Miller, R. 2014. *Engineers build models*. New York: Crabtree.
Summary: Clear, concise text and photographs featuring child engineers introduce the importance of building models in engineering. Featured models include map models, diagrams, blueprints, and three-dimensional models.

Rey, H. A. 2015. *Curious George discovers the Sun*. New York: HMH Books for Young Readers.
Summary: On the hottest day of summer, Curious George and his friends experience a blackout across the whole city. George learns all about sunlight and solar energy as he helps to save the day. Includes a glossary and activities.

Sherman, J. 2004. *Sunshine: A book about sunlight*. Minneapolis: Picture Window Books.
Summary: Simple text and colorful illustrations describe how the Sun heats Earth and causes our weather. It also explains rainbows, day and night, and moonlight.

Name: _____

Comparing Temperatures

Directions: Write the names of four different outside surfaces in the "Surface" column. Your teacher will measure the temperature of each surface in the shade and in the sun. Write the temperatures in the chart.

Surface	Temperature in Shade (°F)	Temperature in Sun (°F)
1.		
2.		
3.		
4.		

Circle the higher temperature for each surface.

Which was hotter: the surfaces in the sun or in the shade?

_____

Name: _____

Sun and Shade

Before Reading True or False		After Reading True or False
_____	1. The Sun is a star.	_____
_____	2. The Sun is made of rock.	_____
_____	3. The Sun gives off heat and light.	_____
_____	4. Plants need the Sun's light to grow.	_____
_____	5. Blocked sunlight makes a shadow called shade.	_____

In the space below, draw a picture of something you saw outside that made shade.

National Science Teaching Association

Name: _____

Keep It Cool
Design Challenge

Challenge: Design a structure to provide a place to cool off on the playground.

Draw your model. Show the Sun in your picture.

Which ice cube took longer to melt? (circle)

In the model   In the sun

Did your model work? _____

How do you know?

_____

_____

Name: _____

STEM Everywhere

Dear Families,

At school, we have been learning about **how the Sun warms Earth's surface.**
We made models of shade structures to reduce the warming effect of sunlight
on an area. To find out more, ask your learner the following questions and
discuss their answers:

- What did you learn?
- What was your favorite part of the lesson?
- What are you still wondering?

At home, you can experiment to find out what would be better to wear on a
hot day—a shirt made of dark fabric or light fabric. This experiment should be
done in a sunny spot on a warm day. You will need the following materials:

- 2 clear plastic containers
- 1 black T-shirt
- 1 white T-shirt

- 2 ice cubes the same size and shape
- 1 watch or timer

Lay the T-shirts next to each other in the sun. Place an ice cube in each
container, and place the containers on the T-shirts. Then, record the time it
takes for each ice cube to melt completely. While you are waiting, you can
feel the T-shirts with your hand and to see if you can feel a difference in
temperature.

Black T-Shirt	White T-Shirt
_____ min.	_____ min.

Which T-shirt would be better to wear on a hot day? Why?

_____

_____

National Science Teaching Association